Play it Cool

trumpet

James Rae

Ten easy pieces for B♭ trumpet and piano

www.universaledition.com

vienna · london · new york

UE 21 265

ISMN 979-0-008-07549-0
UPC 8-03452-02281-7
ISBN 978-3-7024-2740-5

Preface

Designed for the beginner, this collection of pieces provides stimulating performance material in various styles at the easiest possible level. The accompaniments (piano or CD) provide a good solid backing and will inspire the soloist to play with energy and enthusiasm. I have made much deliberate use of the repetition of phrases, as I feel that this is the best way for pupils to absorb new rhythms. This approach, together with the strong support given by the accompaniments, will develop confidence, which is an essential aspect of any musical performance.

Not only is *Play it Cool* suitable for group tuition, it is, in addition, ideal as elementary ensemble material as these ten pieces are also available for other instruments.

James Rae

Vorwort

Diese Sammlung von Stücken ist für Anfänger gedacht und bietet anregendes Aufführungsmaterial in verschiedenen Stilen auf einfachstem Niveau. Die gute solide Begleitung (Klavier oder CD) ermuntert den Solisten, mit Energie und Begeisterung zu spielen. Ich habe absichtlich die Phrasen häufig wiederholt, da ich glaube, dass die Schüler dadurch neue Rhythmen am besten aufnehmen. Zusammen mit der starken Unterstützung durch die Begleitung wird diese Methode das Selbstvertrauen stärken, das ein wesentlicher Aspekt jeder musikalischen Aufführung ist.

Play it Cool ist nicht nur für den Gruppenunterricht geeignet, sondern darüber hinaus auch ideal für Grundstufen-Ensembles, da diese zehn Stücke auch für andere Instrumente verfügbar sind.

James Rae

Préface

Ce recueil de pièces est destiné aux débutants et offre un corpus d'exécution stimulant dans différents styles, et cela dans le niveau le plus simple. L'accompagnement solide (piano ou CD) encourage le soliste à jouer avec énergie et enthousiasme. J'ai intentionellement répété fréquemment les phrases car je pense que, ce faisant, les élèves sont le mieux à même d'enregistrer de nouveaux rythmes. Avec le concours du solide appui que produit l'accompagnement, cette méthode renforcera la confiance en soi qui est un aspect essentiel de toute exécution musicale.

Play it Cool n'est pas seulement adapté à la leçon de groupe mais s'avère également idéal pour les ensembles débutants car ces dix pièces sont aussi disponibles pour d'autres instruments.

James Rae

Contents • Inhalt • Table des Matières

Each piece is fully recorded with a professional soloist for listening and learning. The track following provides the accompaniment minus the solo for playing along.

Jedes Stück wurde zum Anhören und Lernen vollständig aufgenommen, wobei ein professioneller Solist die Solostimme spielt. Der darauf folgende CD-Track dient dem Play-Along Spielen; man hört nur die Begleitung ohne den Solisten.

Chaque pièce a été totalement enregistrée pour l'écoute et l'étude; un soliste professionnel joue la partie soliste. La piste de CD qui suit sert à l'exécution Play-Along ; on entend seulement l'accompagnement sans le soliste.

 **Track 2/3**

Rum Point

JAMES RAE

*This piece requires a very solid pulse. Count all your note-lengths
very carefully and don't be tempted to rush. Keep it steady!*

*Dieses Stück bedarf eines sehr starken Pulses. Spiele den
vorgeschriebenen Rhythmus ganz genau und achte darauf, nicht zu laufen.
Spiele alles gleichmäßig!*

*Cette pièce exige une pulsation très forte. Joue le rythme
prescrit avec une grande exactitude et fais attention de ne pas accélérer.
La force réside dans le calme et la régularité!*

Universal Edition UE 21 265

 **Track 4/5** # Lazy Cat Blues

JAMES RAE

This piece is a typical example of a slow 12 bar blues. Play it with a totally 'laid back' feel and watch your counting on the tied quaver/minim rhythms. Really take your time with this one and don't be tempted to speed up. The slower, the better!

Dieses Stück ist ein typisches Beispiel für einen langsamen 12-taktigen Blues. Spiele ihn mit einem „Laid back feel" und achte auf die Rhythmen mit den übergebundenen Achtelnoten. Lasse dir in diesem Stück wirklich Zeit und versuche, nicht schneller zu werden. Je langsamer, desto besser!

Cette pièce est un exemple typique de blues lent de 12 mesures. Joue-le avec un « Laid back feel » et fais attention aux rythmes avec les croches surliées. Dans cette pièce, prends vraiment ton temps et essaie de ne pas accélérer. Plus c'est lent, mieux c'est !

UE 21 265

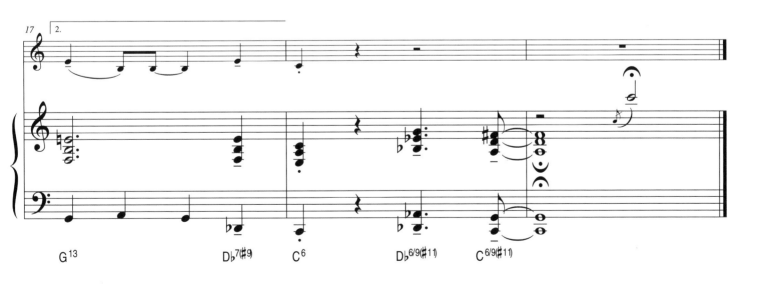

Wimbledon Waltz

JAMES RAE

Play this piece as smoothly as possible with no sharp edges. Aim for nice long phrases and always count the dotted minims accurately.

Spiele dieses Stück so gebunden wie möglich und ohne scharfe Kanten. Achte auf schöne lange Phrasen und halte die punktierten Halben Noten genau aus.

Joue cette pièce aussi liée que possible et sans contours abrupts. Observe les longues et belles phrases et respecte la valeur des blanches pointées.

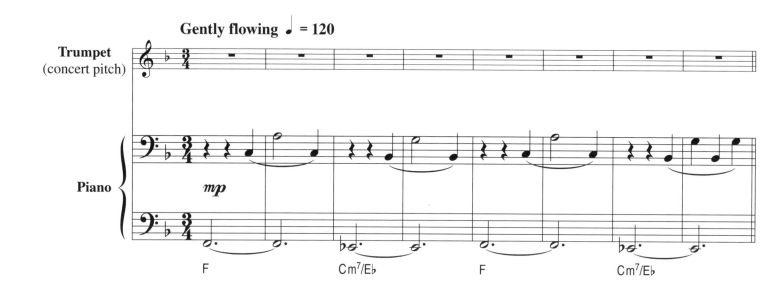

Track 8/9

Hard Graft

JAMES RAE

*Always maintain a solid beat throughout this piece and try to
achieve a sense of building towards a climax at bar 20.*

Bemühe dich in diesem Stück immer um einen starken Puls und versuche,
den Höhepunkt in Takt 20 gut vorzubereiten.

*Dans cette pièce, efforce-toi de conserver une forte pulsation et tente
de bien préparer le sommet de la mesure 20.*

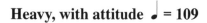

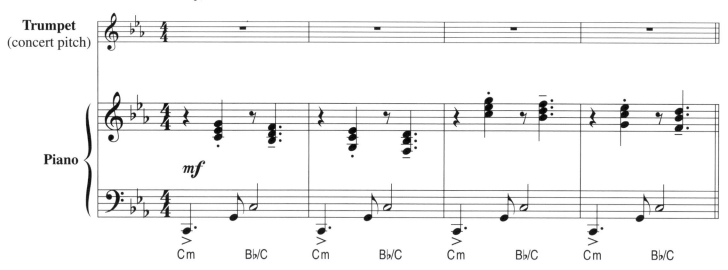

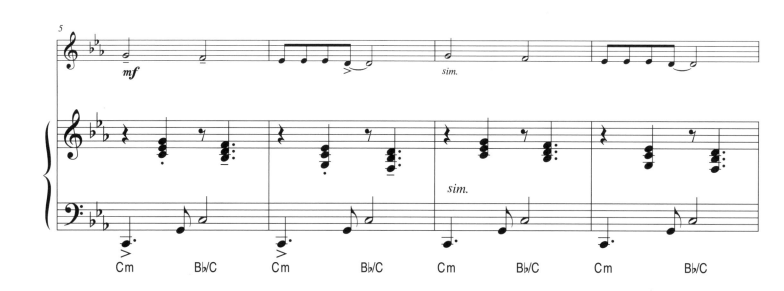

UE 21 265

 **Track 10/11**

The Guv'nor

JAMES RAE

*Lots of controlled power required here! Observe all the articulation carefully
and always play the accents strongly, as if you really mean business!*

Hier ist jede Menge kontrollierter Kraft erforderlich! Beachte alle Artikulationszeichen genau
und hebe die Akzente immer stark hervor, so als ob du es wirklich ernst meinst!

*Ici une grande dose de force contrôlée est nécessaire ! Observe précisément tous les signes d'articulation
et fais toujours ressortir les accents, pour qu'on entende que tu le prends vraiment au sérieux !*

Track 12/13

Curtain Up!

JAMES RAE

*This piece is typical of a theatrical opening number. Feel the strong two beats
in a bar – not four. Aim for a sense of lively excitement throughout.*

Dieses Stück ist eine typische Eröffnungsnummer im Theater. Fühle die zwei starken Zählzeiten
im Takt – nicht vier. Bemühe dich durchgehend um ein Gefühl lebendiger Aufregung.

*Cette pièce est un numéro typique d'ouverture au théâtre. Tu dois sentir les deux temps forts en
mesure – pas quatre. Efforce toi d'établir du début à la fin un sentiment d'excitation joyeuse.*

Track 14/15

Bruno's Tune

JAMES RAE

The essence of 'funk' music is in its powerful driving energy which is usually the result of placing a solid melody over an intricate rhythmic accompaniment. Always maintain a firm pulse when you play this piece so that your melody can fit neatly over the backing.

Das Wesen der „Funk"-Musik besteht in ihrer mächtigen vorwärts treibenden Energie, die gewöhnlich durch Überlagerung einer kniffligen rhythmischen Begleitung mit einer soliden Melodie entsteht. Bemühe dich um einen regelmäßigen starken Puls, wenn du dieses Stück spielst, damit deine Melodie sauber mit der Begleitung koordiniert werden kann.

L'essence de la « Funk music » réside dans son énergie puissamment poussante qui naît habituellement par la superposition d'un accompagnement rythmique délicat sur une solide mélodie. Essaie d'obtenir, lorsque tu joues cette mélodie, une forte pulsation régulière, pour que ta mélodie puisse être proprement coordonnée avec l'accompagnement.

UE 21 265

Rumba

JAMES RAE

*The Rumba is a Latin American Dance with the same repeated
rhythmic accompaniment in each bar. Pay special attention to the
slurs and always count the dotted minim lengths accurately.*

Die Rumba ist ein lateinamerikanischer Tanz mit einer in jedem Takt
gleichen rhythmischen Begleitung. Beachte besonders die Bindebögen und
halte die punktierten Halben Noten genau aus.

*La rumba est une danse d'Amérique latine avec un accompagnement
rythmique identique dans chaque mesure. Tiens particulièrement compte des
liaisons et respecte précisément la durée des blanches pointées.*

Track 18/19

Gate 24

JAMES RAE

*Cool is the name of the game here. Aim to play in long, smooth
phrases observing all slurs carefully. Pay particular attention
to the accidentals in the section from bars 21 to 33.*

Cool sein ist hier der Reiz an der Sache. Bemühe dich um lange geschmeidige
Phrasen und befolge die Bindebögen genau. Beachte besonders die Vorzeichen im
Abschnitt zwischen den Takten 21 und 33.

*Etre cool est ici le charme de la chose. Essaie d'obtenir de longues phrases
souples et observé exactement les liaisons. Observe particulièrement les altérations
dans le passage compris entre les mesures 21 et 33.*

Blowin' Cool

JAMES RAE

*Really let your hair down and 'roll in the dirt' with this one! Pay special
attention to the section from bar 15 where the accompaniment cuts out
and you are left high and dry. Always keep the quavers swinging.*

Hier kannst du wirklich alles herauslassen, um dieses Stück lebendig zu interpretieren!
Achte besonders auf den in Takt 15 beginnenden Abschnitt, in dem die Begleitung pausiert und
du ganz allein musizierst. Spiele die Achtelnoten immer swingend.

*Tu peux ici vraiment tout faire sortir pour interpréter cette pièce de manière vivante!
Fais particulièrement attention au passage commençant sur la mesure 15 : l'accompagnement
fait une pause et tu joues tout seul. Joue toujours les croches en swing.*